... and a beret.

Every morning my Daddy goes to work ...

My Daddy Is A Soldier

For Mini P from Granny Gezza

A huge big thanks to Shay and Michael; without them the book would never have got off the ground.

To Grammy for believing in the dream.
Tana and Paul for all their help and encouragement and to Dad - it's all in the genes!
Dankeschön to Heidrun Schaffner, Paul Baldwin, Carol Yates and Stu Routley.
To all the people who allowed me to pick their brains, it was greatly appreciated.

And finally to the Afghan Appeal Fund Committee for sponsoring my book, thank you very much.

A catalogue record for this book is available from the British Library
ISBN 978-90-813731-1-1

Printed in The Netherlands by AF

My Daddy is a soldier; he wears a uniform ...

... on his bike.

Daddy will be home tonight ...

... for his tea.

Daddy has to work far away, for a long time...

... and I have to be a good girl for Mummy.

Daddy packs his bags ...

... and I help him.

Daddy leaves early in the morning ...

... I wave him goodbye.

Daddy is not home for Christmas ...

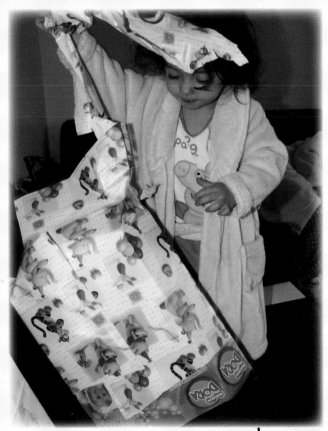

... he sends me a present.

Daddy is not home for my birthday ...

... I send him some cake.

Daddy is not home for the summer ...

... Mummy takes me to the beach.

Daddy is not home when Grandad comes to visit...

... Grandad takes me to see the donkeys.

Every Sunday ...

... we write blueys.

Daddy phones and says ...

... he is coming home.

Daddy is coming home ...

... in one more sleep.

Daddy is home...

... I love my Daddy.